Stoats al

Robbie McDonal

*Quercus, School of Biological Sciences, Queen's University Belfast, Belfast BT9 7BL, Northern Ireland
[+]School of Biological Sciences, University of Bristol, Woodland Road, Bristol BS8 1UG, UK.

Contents

Stoats and weasels
By Robbie McDonald and Stephen Harris

Published by The Mammal Society
1997 Edition, reprinted in Jan 2006

The Mammal Society
Registered Charity No. 278918
Registered Office:
The Mammal Society
2B Inworth Street
London
SW11 3EP

ISBN 0 906282 61 6

This is one of a series of booklets on British mammals
published by The Mammal Society

Drawings by Sarah Wroot

Typesetting and printing by SP Press, Units 1-2,
Mendip Vale Trading Estate, Cheddar Business Park,
Wedmore Road, Cheddar, Somerset BS27 3EL

Reputation, recognition and relatives

*Were they equal in size to lions and tigers, the human race would be in
danger of total extirpation: for it is well known that weasels are the most
ferocious and bloodthirsty creatures upon the earth.*

Captain Mayne Reid, 1872

**Skirmishing stoats
and weasel words**

There are few mammals in Britain that are as widespread and well known,
but as poorly understood, as weasels and stoats. Many biologists have
found their mercurial behaviour fascinating and, all too frequently,
frustrating. Despite the difficulty of studying weasels and stoats they are
endowed with a fearsome reputation, as indicated by the writings of
Captain Mayne Reid in 1872. They have suffered at the hands of several
authors, the most notable of whom is Kenneth Grahame, writer of Wind in
the Willows. In his children's classic "skirmishing stoats and bloodthirsty
weasels" laid siege to Toad Hall evicting Mr. Toad. Many other writers
represent them as cunning, devious and treacherous. "Weasel words" are a
bye-word for double dealing and a dirty old man is sometimes referred to
as a "randy old stoat".

*Fleeting. The briefest
glimpse of a stoat popping
out of a hole or dashing
across a road is often as
much as people have seen
of these mercurial
creatures.*

Weasels and stoats are efficient predators and are bold beyond their size.
They are aggressive and voracious, but they are graceful, inquisitive and
fearless in self-defence. The root of their bad reputation lies almost
certainly in historical rivalries with man. They are predators of poultry and
game and have been trapped by gamekeepers for decades. However, other
cultures look more favourably on weasels and stoats because of their
rodent catching ability. They can also be partially tamed and can even
make fascinating pets.

**Family and close
relatives**

Weasels *Mustela nivalis* and stoats *Mustela erminea* belong to the family
of carnivores known as the Mustelidae. The "weasel family" has a total of
67 species, divided into five sub-families; true badgers Melinae, the honey
badger Mellivorinae, skunks Mephitinae, otters Lutrinae and the true
weasels Mustelinae. There are two recognised sub-species of weasel, the
common weasel *Mustela nivalis vulgaris* and the least weasel *Mustela
nivalis nivalis*. Both sub-species have a wide distribution across the

northern part of Eurasia and North America, though the smaller least weasel prevails in the far north. In a few limited areas, the two sub-species of weasel coexist, though in Great Britain we only have the common weasel. Weasels are absent from Ireland, but there is a distinct sub-species of Irish stoat *Mustela erminea hibernica*, which is sometimes confusingly known as a weasel!

To confuse the picture further, there are other species also known as weasels. Probably the closest relative to the British stoat and weasel is the long-tailed weasel *Mustela frenata* which lives in north and central America, and in some areas coexists with stoats and weasels. There is also a range of little known weasel species across the world including the Egyptian weasel *Mustela subpalmata* which used to be thought of as a subspecies but is now considered a species in its own right, the barefoot weasel *Mustela nudipes* found in south east Asia and the recently discovered Colombian weasel *Mustela felipei*. Close British relatives to weasels and stoats include polecats *Mustela putorius* and feral American mink *Mustela vison*, both of which share the smaller species' reputation for aggression and voraciousness.

Weaselly good looks

Their sleek, sinuous shape characterises all members of the weasel sub-family. They are well adapted to pursuing small mammal prey into their burrows. A weasel's head is the widest part of the body and if that can be squeezed into a mouse hole, then the rest of its body will follow. Often the only view had of a weasel or stoat is of its head poking out from a burrow or crevice in a stone wall. There is an old wives' tale that the head of a weasel may pass through a wedding ring, and there are pictures to prove it. However, despite the weasel's small size, this was probably a very small weasel's skull and the ring of a very large old wife!

Are weasels weasily recognised?

It can sometimes be difficult to tell weasels and stoats apart. Both animals have pale bellies and are a chestnut

Recognising stoats and weasels. Stoats (right) have a long tail with a black bushy tip, whereas weasels (left) have a short tail that is uniform in colour and does not have a bushy tip. Weasels also have an irregular margin between the dark back and the pale belly whereas in British stoats the line is straight. Adult females of both species are always smaller than males.

brown colour, though this varies, and many stoats are more of a sandy colour. However, stoats are larger than weasels. A large male stoat can be three times, and a female two times, the weight of a male weasel. The stoat's tail has a distinctive black tip and is much longer than a weasel's which is uniform in colour. The belly of the stoat is a more creamy colour than the whiter bellied weasel and the line separating the pale bellies and dark backs is clearly demarcated in British stoats, while it is irregular in weasels. The belly pattern of weasels, together with the darker spots amongst the white, can even be used to identify individuals.

Field signs

Field signs of weasels and stoats are found only rarely. Their droppings, or scats, are long, very thin and twisted. They usually contain fur or feathers and can be found at dens and on prominent rocks or logs. Their dens are usually made in the burrows of their prey, taken over after eating the occupant and making a bed out of their fur. Weasel nests, characterised by droppings and half-eaten prey remains, can occasionally be found under corrugated iron sheets left in grassland and in collapsed stone walls. In areas where there is permanent snow in winter, weasels and stoats make nests under the snow but above ground level. The nests, which are revealed as the snow melts, have even been used as an index of weasel and stoat abundance in some studies.

Field signs. Stoat (right) and weasel (left) tracks can be found occasionally in mud or in snow. Droppings, or scats, are long, thin and twisted. They contain fur and feather remains and can be found on prominent stones or logs and outside dens.

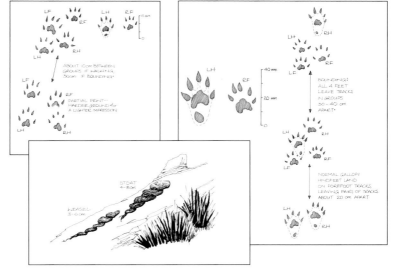

It is usually difficult to make out stoat and weasel tracks, but the weaving paths they take while dashing along hedgerows and fence lines can sometimes be seen in soft mud or fresh snow. Snow tracking has been used by Scandinavian biologists to work out weasel and stoat ranges, and gamekeepers in Scotland and northern England have tracked stoats for miles over snow covered moors.

Winter whitening

Ermine cloaks

In Britain, a major difference between stoats and weasels is that stoats moult into a white coat in winter, whereas weasels almost always stay brown. The stoat's white coat, with the distinctive black tip of its tail remaining, is known as ermine and is famous for its use in the ceremonial robes of nobles and judges. Pure ermine-coated stoats are mainly found in Scotland, Wales and the west of Britain. In other areas, a few stoats can turn partially white but patches of brown usually remain. This partial whitening, where animals take on a mottled or piebald appearance, may be seen as far south as Wiltshire and Essex, though most southern stoats stay brown even during the occasional severe winter.

Why whiten in winter?

John, 1st Duke of Roxburgh. Robes made of ermine, with the characteristic black spots from the stoats' tails, were reserved for the highest nobles in the land.

Winter whitening is a response to long periods of snow cover and has evolved to provide camouflage from larger predators. Regions that have a lot of snow are, therefore, the most likely to have white stoats in winter. However, it is a combination of several factors that controls the process of winter whitening. In general terms, the geographical borderline between go-white and stay-brown stoats can be predicted by winter temperatures, since the coldest regions usually have the longest period of snow cover. The temperature the stoat experiences during the autumn moulting period affects hormones in the brain and controls whether or not fur grown in the autumn is supplied with the pigments that colour it brown. If temperatures fall below a certain threshold, the pigment supply is turned off and the new fur grows through white. Whatever its colour, the winter coat is still thicker and warmer than the summer coat and the insulation quality of the fur is not affected by its colour.

The fur trade

Ermine and the white fur of least weasels, known as *lettice*, have always been amongst the most highly prized pelts. As early as the Middle Ages, Viking and Byzantine traders were exporting Scandinavian and Russian ermine to the courts of England and southern Europe. Richard I paid £12 to have ermine blankets sent out from England while he was on Crusade. Indeed, a Royal Decree of 1188 forbade crusading knights to wear ermine, so the precious furs could be retained for the highest nobles in the land.

The trade in furs, including ermine, was once so valuable that vast areas of Canada were opened up by traders, mainly from the Hudson's Bay Company, seeking sources of prime pelts for European markets. In the 1906 London fur sales, 80 000 ermine pelts were sold in March alone. The highest price paid was seven shillings and six pence for a Siberian skin in prime white with no hint of yellow. Such prices were not unheard of when the fur industry was at its height. Today, the fur industry has changed greatly and ermine is now rarely seen except in the ceremonial robes of judges and nobility. In May 2005 at the North Bay Fur Harvesters' auctions in Canada, 2240 ermine pelts sold for an average of only £2.00, while the top price was just over £3.50. As a result, professional fur trappers now concentrate on more valuable pelts such as mink, marten and otter.

 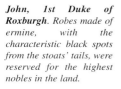

The cue for actually starting the moult from summer to winter coat is not temperature but day length. As winter approaches, days shorten and a separate set of hormonal changes in the animal's brain start the moulting process. At high latitudes winter days grow shorter faster than at lower latitudes and, as a result, stoats moult rapidly into full ermine white. Countries like Britain lie in regions at intermediate latitudes with changeable climates. In such countries, stoats moult over a longer period and should temperatures vary during the moulting season, the resultant changes in the animal's hormones can alter the moult pattern and produce a mottled or piebald appearance.

Several interesting experiments have shown that even when exposed to cold, snowy conditions, stoats from warm areas that usually stay brown continue to do so. Similarly, stoats from areas where winter whitening is the norm still turn white after being moved to milder climes. These experiments indicate that in addition to temperature and day length, the stoat's genes also control whether it turns white.

Piebald and mottled. Stoats in changeable climates frequently moult into a partial ermine coat in winter. In colder regions, stoats turn pure white and only the black tip to the tail remains.

White genes for females

The genes that control whitening in stoats are also thought to be linked to the chromosomes that control gender, since a greater proportion of females than males tend to grow an ermine coat in winter. This is because females have two copies of the female sex chromosome and on at least one copy they are likely to have the dominant go-white gene. This is particularly significant for female stoats, since it can sometimes be useful to be able to grow an ermine coat in normally mild areas so that they can be camouflaged during an unexpectedly snowy winter. On the other hand, male stoats tend to turn white less frequently than females, since they have only one copy of the female sex chromosome and there is a greater chance that the recessive stay-brown gene will be expressed. Staying brown can also be useful during the odd mild winter in normally snowy regions. This sex-linked mechanism is particularly advantageous in regions with changeable climates, like Britain, since at least one or two individuals from a single litter of stoats have a good chance of survival, however unpredictable the winters are.

Why no white weasels?

For some unknown reason, weasels need a longer period of snow cover than stoats before they turn white. Therefore, the threshold for whitening in weasels is a good deal further north than the critical latitude for stoats. Least weasels, which live at higher latitudes than common weasels, usually turn white in winter. This difference between whitening in common weasels and least weasels is the result of differences in their genetic make up. In parts of Sweden, least and common weasels coexist. In this narrow region, even though they live at the same latitude, least weasels turn white while common weasels stay brown. This suggests that common weasels evolved in warmer climes than least weasels and the two sub-species have only recently met at a transition point between their two ranges. British common weasels evolved in mild climates, so it is their genetic heritage that prevents them from turning white.

Distribution and coexistence

Widespread but elusive. Weasels are seen only rarely, but together with stoats, they are Britain's most common native carnivores and occur in every mainland county.

Stoats and weasels occur throughout the northern Holarctic region above 40 degrees north, though weasels also occur as far south as North Africa. Although rarely seen, they are Britain's most common native carnivores. Current estimates suggest that there are about half a million of each species in Britain before the breeding season starts. They occur in every mainland county but are very rarely seen in urban areas. They are found in a wide range of habitats, including moors, marshes, woodland and farmland. Stoats tend to be found more frequently at high altitudes than weasels, but weasels take more readily to the conifer forests that now cover much of Britain's uplands.

Competition and coexistence

Stoats and weasels are present together only on a few of the offshore islands in Britain; Skye, Anglesey, Sheppey and the Isle of Wight. Stoats are present on other islands; Islay, Jura, Mull, the Isle of Man (where, like Ireland, they are confusingly known as weasels), and there are occasional records of stoats from the Channel Islands, especially Jersey. Curiously, weasels are absent from all of these islands. This peculiar distribution is due to fundamental differences in their biology. Stoats, being the larger,

8

Upland refuges. The rough grassland found in young plantations and forest rides harbour large field vole populations and provide a rich source of food for weasels.

Stoats and weasels in New Zealand

In 1883 New Zealand's Chief Rabbit Inspector instigated a policy of transporting and releasing stoats and weasels from Britain into New Zealand. His aim was to reduce the costly damage to grazing caused by rabbits. The first shipments of animals arrived the year after and for the next ten to 15 years stoats and weasels were introduced by the shipload.

Stoats flourished under the full protection of the law and they quickly spread to areas miles away from the introduction sites. Unfortunately, the Chief Inspector's plan was an unmitigated disaster. While the stoats ate some rabbits, mice and rats, they failed to control their numbers. Worse still, they have been a major cause of the decline of many endemic species. The New Zealand Government now spends millions of dollars trying to work out the best way of controlling the impact of stoats on native birds, such as mohua, takahe, kiwi and even penguins. Eggs baited with poisons, intensive trapping and habitat management are all applied in areas where the birds are most vulnerable. The stoats also prey on endemic lizards, wetas (giant ground crickets) and freshwater crayfish.

As for the weasels, despite being introduced in similar numbers, weasels found the food available to them in New Zealand too different from their usual diet and they suffered from competition with the stoats. Large populations never became established and weasels are now one of the rarest mammals in the country.

more adaptable predator with a broader diet, are able to cope with the variation in prey availability that occurs on small islands. Stoats are also aggressive competitors and will interfere with weasels, stealing their food or even killing them. On the other hand, weasels are well adapted to exploiting small mammals, especially voles, since they can hunt in rodent burrows. Weasels are dependent on the presence of voles, but also need a variety of habitats in order to avoid interference from stoats. In times of food shortage, competition between stoats and weasels living in restricted areas has ended in the extinction of one or other species. In the long term and in variable habitat, the two species can coexist, since in a changing environment it is sometimes beneficial to be an aggressive, adaptable competitor like the stoat, whereas at other times and places it is better to be a specialist predator like the weasel.

Body size

Despite their larger-than-life reputation, weasels and stoats are the world's smallest carnivores and it is their small size which governs most aspects of their biology. Small size is an adaptation to pursuing small mammals down their tunnels. However, there are also evolutionary incentives to grow large in order to minimise the risks associated with attacking larger prey, maintain large territories and defend yourself against competitors and other predators. This means that body size in weasels and stoats is hugely variable between areas where differing ecological conditions exist.

How big are stoats and weasels? These figures come from animals killed by gamekeepers on estates across Great Britain between 1995 and 1997 and include juveniles and pregnant females.

		Body weight (g)		Body length (mm)		Tail length (mm)		Skull length (mm)	
		Males	Females	Males	Females	Males	Females	Males	Females
Weasels	Average	121	66	215	184	49	40	39.5	34.6
	Range	73-195	48-107	180-248	169-196	30-62	28-49	35.8-44.4	32.4-36.6
	No. measured	381	77	381	77	379	77	341	62
Stoats	Average	342	227	286	258	101	89	50.9	46.5
	Range	124-498	115-323	209-318	220-283	56-127	55-109	46.4-54.5	42.6-49.5
	No. measured	514	301	505	294	448	259	397	241

Adult male stoats and weasels are always larger than adult females. In most cases, males are about half as heavy again as females, though this varies between regions. Why there should be such large differences in size between the sexes has been the topic of much discussion among biologists. Initially, theories centred around apparent differences in diet. Females avoided competition with males by eating smaller prey and so it was beneficial to be smaller. Unfortunately, this is something of a chicken and egg argument. Which came first, smaller body size or smaller prey?

Foraging. Weasels investigate every nook and cranny in pursuit of prey. Their small size means they can pursue small rodents right into their tunnels.

In fact, the solution is a combination of factors to do with both feeding and reproduction. It is generally advantageous for a male to grow large so that he can compete successfully with other males. That way he stands a better chance of mating with more females and fathering a greater number of young. In contrast, it is important for a female to stay small, so that she can reproduce efficiently by devoting all her time and energy to successfully rearing her young. Being small enough to get into all small mammal burrows means that she has a dependable source of prey when her needs are greatest. Staying small also keeps metabolic costs low so that more energy can be devoted to reproduction. Male stoats and weasels have no part in rearing young and so do not have the same pressure to maintain small body size.

Geographic variation in body size. Both stoats and weasels are extremely variable in body size throughout their range. British stoats are particularly large, and are always larger than British weasels. European weasels increase in size with decreasing latitude, and North African weasels are as large as our stoats.

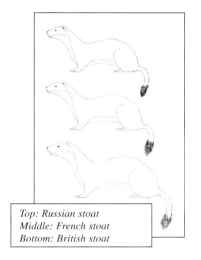

Top: Russian stoat
Middle: French stoat
Bottom: British stoat

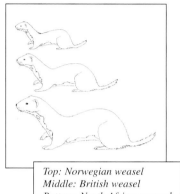

Top: Norwegian weasel
Middle: British weasel
Bottom: North African weasel

Weasels don't obey the rules

There are, however, other factors acting on the body size of all weasels and stoats. One general theory about mammals is that body size increases with increasing latitude. Bergmann's Rule, as this principle is known, is based on the conservation of energy in harsh environments. Large animals on average have a low surface area to volume ratio which means they are better at conserving body heat, and so have proportionally lower energetic costs. One might expect weasels and stoats, with their long, thin body shape and high surface area to volume ratio, to fit into this rule. However, the opposite is true. Both stoats and weasels living near the poles tend to be smaller than their counterparts further south. The largest weasels are found in North Africa, where they are as large as our stoats. The answer to this conundrum again lies with their specialist habit of preying on small mammals and pursuing them into their burrows. In the far north, weasels and stoats spend much of the winter pursuing their quarry in tunnels under the snow. They are, therefore, insulated from the extreme temperatures and wind chill that other mammals must survive during a polar winter.

Stoat downsizing?

The picture gets more confusing if we look at stoats and weasels in the British Isles. Weasels tend to be larger in Scotland while stoats tend to be larger in the south of England. Equally curiously, stoats in Ireland, where weasels are absent, have long been thought to be smaller than mainland British stoats. This was explained by the absence of weasels and the "downsizing" of stoats in order to exploit part of the weasel niche. However, stoats in the south of Ireland are as large as mainland British animals and it is only the northern Irish stoats that are small. This odd pattern may even have been further complicated by introductions of British stock to the south.

No silver spoons for stoats

Recent studies in New Zealand demonstrated a curious turnaround for factors affecting body size and survival in stoats. Normally, it would be expected that animals born in times of plenty would grow faster and have a better chance of survival than those born when food was scarce. This is known as the "silver-spoon" effect since the young born in good times are supposed to be given a head start in life. It is true that stoats of both sexes grow larger and faster when food is plentiful. However, females also rear larger litters when food is in good supply. This means that the young stoats born in times of plenty may grow quickly, but then face intense competition for resources when they leave the nest. The largest males also have the greatest energy requirements and may starve before taking advantage of the reproductive benefits that accrue later in life. Ironically, the silver-spoon stoats are therefore more likely to die young than those born in times of shortage, when the competition is not so tough. Body size, like many other evolutionary characters, is certainly a constant juggling act between environmental conditions and a whole suite of conflicting interests, and there is great potential for further studies in this area.

Food and foraging

Guts and droppings

Surprisingly, the diet of stoats and weasels has been little studied. Samples of gut contents may be collected from dead animals, either killed by gamekeepers or on the roads, or from droppings collected from dens or during live trapping. The undigested contents, usually fur or feather remains, can be identified using a microscope and a collection of fur from known sources. The fur of lagomorphs (rabbits and hares) and shrews can be easily identified but it is difficult to distinguish between the different species of these groups, and it is also tricky to distinguish different species of voles. Added to this is the fact that many guts are empty to start with and much of the partially digested material is completely unrecognisable.

Changes in the diet of stoats between the 1960s and the 1990s. The relative importance of rabbits in the diet has increased as rabbit numbers recovered after myxomatosis. Small rodents and game birds are now eaten less frequently.

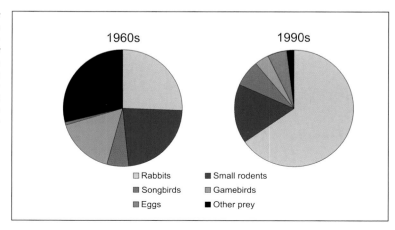

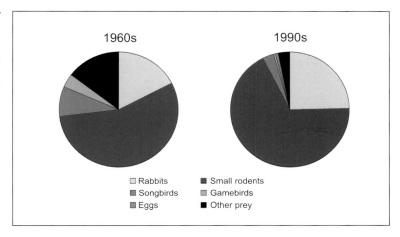

Changes in the diet of weasels between the 1960s and the 1990s. Weasels have become more specialised on small mammals, while the importance of birds has decreased.

All this may explain why there has only been two national studies of the diet of both stoats and weasels, in the 1960s and the 1990s. This work and several more localised studies have all highlighted the importance of small mammals in the diet of both stoats and weasels. For weasels living on farmland, as most do, field voles are the most important food item but bank voles, wood mice, rabbits and birds are also taken. Although stoats evolved to eat small rodents, they are now mainly predators of rabbits and most studies find that rabbit is by far the most important item on the stoat menu. Stoats tend to eat more birds than weasels, perhaps because they can more readily catch and kill large game birds and waders.

Weasels smell better than they look

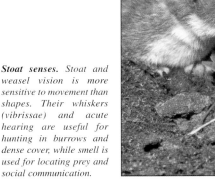

Stoat senses. Stoat and weasel vision is more sensitive to movement than shapes. Their whiskers (vibrissae) and acute hearing are useful for hunting in burrows and dense cover, while smell is used for locating prey and social communication.

The foraging and hunting behaviour of weasels and stoats is very rarely seen, largely because they spend so much of their time hunting in burrows and under snow. When hunting on the surface, both species are absorbing to watch and it is a rare treat to see these predators in action. The first sight of a hunting stoat or weasel is usually when it stands up on its hind legs. This is probably to get a better smell of its surroundings. The eyesight of most carnivores is extremely sensitive to movements but not to shapes. This means that if you stand stock still when you see a weasel or stoat, it will frequently run right up to you without noticing you. Move, and it will flee instantly. Standing on their hind legs, they can pick up smells on the wind, notice any movements or hear the rustling of prey in the undergrowth.

On the lookout. Attacking a full grown rabbit is a risky business for stoats and even after the kill, they risk their prey being stolen by more dominant stoats or larger predators.

Swimmers and climbers

Weasels and stoats move rapidly when they are foraging. They dash wildly about meadows and woods, nosing under every tussock and into every burrow. In some cases, they actually seem to be trying to scare the voles out of their burrows, driving them into the open where they can be easily caught and killed. Stoats and weasels leave no hole unchecked. They are strong swimmers and excellent climbers, so no bird or squirrel nest is safe. When they encounter a vole or mouse it is killed rapidly with a precision bite to the back of the neck. An encounter with a rabbit, however, is a different matter. Even the largest stoat is still substantially lighter than a full grown rabbit, and there is a real risk of injury.

Vampires?

It is unclear whether large prey are killed by a bite to the spine or by the sheer shock of being attacked. "Stoated" rabbits and birds are sometimes found apparently frozen by fear and rendered incapable of escape. Other prey animals are frequently found abandoned, but with bite wounds to the neck. This has lead to the belief that stoats and weasels suck the blood of their victims. This too is part of the mythology surrounding stoats and weasels. They will certainly lick the blood of their victims as they are dying, but the wounded animals have not been abandoned and the stoat or weasel will not be far away, intending to cache its prey for later.

Dance of death

Another widespread belief is that weasels and stoats mesmerise their prey with a wild cavorting dance. They entrance their prey by acting in a madcap way, leaping, and twisting around as though possessed. The prey is curious and approaches nearer, whilst the stoat or weasel remains slyly attentive throughout its mad "fits". When they are close enough, the pretence of insanity is dropped and the predator seizes its dumbfounded prey. It sounds outrageous, and it is certainly an odd strategy for a predator to adopt. As a result, some biologists think that it is not so much a strategy for prey capture, but is a response to the irritation caused by a parasite that commonly infects the brain case of weasels and stoats.

Prey switching

Weasel diet, naturally enough, changes according to the availability of prey. In Wytham Woods, near Oxford, predation by weasels was responsible for the failure of about 20% of tit nests over a thirty year period. The evidence was unequivocal, since the nest boxes were equipped with automatic cameras. What was interesting was that weasels turned their attention to the nests under two sets of circumstances - when the density of rodents was low or when the density of nesting birds was particularly high. Either set of circumstances meant that it became efficient for the weasels to change their foraging strategy to focus on the nest boxes as a source of food.

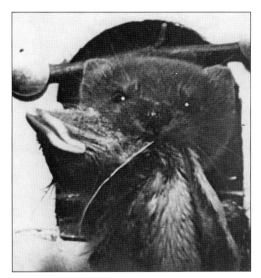

Caught in the act. Automatic cameras snapped this weasel raiding a tit nest box in Wytham Woods. Predation of nest boxes was particularly serious when rodent prey was scarce or nesting birds were especially common.

This "prey switching" is a common phenomenon in carnivores and similar patterns were found on the Sussex Downs, where vole densities and their prevalence in weasel diet were closely related. When vole numbers were high they increased in importance until they formed over 50% of weasel diet. When vole numbers were low, weasels switched to eating birds. Male weasels also showed more seasonal variation in their diet than females, perhaps because their larger ranges and greater size meant that a larger variety of food was available to them.

Prey controls predators

Interestingly, when vole populations crashed on the Sussex study site, as they did every three or four years, the weasels switched prey but still suffered from the loss of their staple food and failed to breed. This emphasises a major factor in the relationship between these small predators and their prey: their numbers are controlled by the prey available to them. In the long term, if food is scarce, weasel and stoat populations will decline or may even become locally extinct. This in part explains why they are such difficult species to study. Populations undergo frequent booms and busts, and if study starts when numbers are low or resident animals are absent, then there is little hope of gathering any field data.

Predators control prey

While prey numbers govern whether weasel and stoat females can breed successfully, it is also apparent that it is a two way relationship. Predators can affect their prey in a number of ways. Experiments in Finland found that if least weasels and stoats were removed from an area, the reproductive output of the voles increased and a greater proportion of females became pregnant. In other words, the risk of predation was preventing voles from breeding. The experiment also found that predators selectively killed female voles and that voles were less mobile when predators were present. A combination of suppressed breeding and selective killing meant that weasels and stoats actually slowed the growth of vole populations.

Predation and predator control

The impact of stoats on populations of their prey will not come as a surprise to many gamekeepers. An individual stoat was once found to have eaten the eggs and chicks from 15 grey partridge nests around four small fields. A biologist studying curlews found that, over three years, 26 out of 59 nests were destroyed by stoats and at least 21 of 39 curlew chicks tagged with radio-transmitters were killed by stoats. Stoats can also kill adult game birds, especially brooding females, and they certainly eat the eggs and chicks of whatever species they come across. The ones they do not eat straight away will be cached for times of shortage.

The impact of weasel predation on game is more debatable. Given the chance, a weasel would certainly take a game bird chick. However, weasels are generally too small to take adult game birds and large eggs are difficult for them to handle. As a result, many gamekeepers regard weasels as much less of a threat than stoats. Most weasels are actually killed as a by-product of efforts to control stoat numbers, since it is difficult to set a trap for a stoat that will not also catch a weasel.

Humane trapping

Because stoats and weasels are not protected in the same way as martens, polecats and other mustelids, they can be killed legally by shooting or using certain traps. Gin traps are now illegal in Britain because their toothed jaws did not kill animals humanely. The approved humane trap that is now most widely used is known as a Fenn or a Springer. Unlike the gin, Fenn traps do not catch the animal by its leg. Instead, they have two steel bars set on a strong spring. When a central pan is disturbed by a passing animal, the bars snap together across its spine. The traps must be checked every day and set in tunnels that other animals, like cats and dogs, cannot get into. Usually, tunnels are dug into hedges and set along walls that are regularly patrolled by stoats and weasels.

Wild game

Many gamekeepers now rely on rearing their birds and this means that predation on wild chicks and eggs by stoats and weasels tends to be less important to them. These gamekeepers now mainly run traps to keep stoats away from the pens where young pheasant and partridge poults are released. It is quite a different matter on estates where the aim is to encourage populations of wild game birds, and predation by stoats is often a significant problem. These wild game estates are now in the minority in lowland England, but several of the larger estates of East Anglia still depend on wild pheasant and partridge to a great extent. In East Anglia and in northern England and Scotland, where red grouse is the main quarry, stoat trapping is still a major part of the gamekeeper's job.

Effects of trapping

Despite the best efforts of gamekeepers to control stoat numbers, most find that the numbers they trap year on year remain fairly constant. There are certainly marked fluctuations and in some years gamekeepers trap fewer

Predator control. Stoat trapping is still an important part of the gamekeeper's job, especially on estates promoting wild game. Here, a gamekeeper is resetting a Fenn trap in a tunnel after catching a stoat.

stoats and weasels than others, while there are also occasional boom years. However, once a consistent trapping programme has become established, there does not appear to be a relationship between trapping success one year and the numbers taken the following year. The best gamekeepers can usually hope for is that their trapping temporarily reduces the numbers of stoats on their beat during the critical periods when birds are nesting or poults are released.

Other mustelids have not fared so well

An interesting comparison can be drawn between the fate of stoats and weasels at the hands of Victorian gamekeepers and that of other mustelids. Pine martens and polecats came close to extinction as a result of widespread poisoning and persecution in the 19th century. Pine martens survived mainly in the rocky uplands of Scotland, while polecats evaded persecution in the Welsh valleys, where gamekeepering was not as intensive. Martens and polecats are now recovering as a result of legal protection. Stoats and weasels have been trapped and shot by gamekeepers for as long as martens and polecats, and in even greater numbers. However, they have never been in any danger of extinction.

This is because stoats and weasels are fast breeders. In contrast to other carnivores, which are long lived, slow breeding species that depend on stability in the environment, stoats and weasels adopt a live fast-die young approach to life. They mature quickly, their litter sizes are large, and most die at an early age. This means they are adapted to withstand very high rates of natural mortality, mainly brought about by unpredictable food supplies. Gamekeepers, therefore, have a great deal of difficulty keeping up with natural levels of mortality, let alone adding to them with their own trapping.

Reproduction

Stoats and weasels are unusual among carnivores for their prodigious reproductive capacity. Weasels usually have a single litter but can produce two litters in years when food is especially plentiful. Stoats capitalise on abundant food resources by producing a single, large litter. However, breeding behaviour and reproduction is also the aspect of their biology which most clearly separates weasels and stoats.

A young weasel. Juvenile stoats and weasels have a large, rounded head with a short nose and more 'fluffy' pelage than adults. Both species mature rapidly and these external signs of youth are quickly lost.

Weasels breed like rabbits!

Female weasels mature at about three to four months of age and, in years of plentiful food, they can breed in their first year. Adult females come into oestrus in February, are mated immediately and, after gestation of about 36 days, give birth to a litter of blind, naked young. Litter size varies according to food supplies. There can be as many as eight kits, but the norm in Britain is five or six. The female's energy demands increase tenfold after she gives birth and starts suckling her young, and she spends the next nine weeks foraging intensely to bring in enough food for herself and the rapidly developing kits. When her first litter are weaned, usually in May, she comes into oestrus again. If sufficient prey are available, both she and her female young can breed again before the autumn. In theory, if she and all her female kits raised six viable young, a single female could produce 30 children and grandchildren in a single year. If she and all her young survived another year and bred twice again, she could have propagated as many as 510 weasels in just two years. In nature this would never happen because natural mortality is very high, but it is a graphic illustration of just how quickly weasels can take advantage of good conditions.

Nine month pregnancy in stoats?

Stoats have evolved a very different reproductive strategy from weasels. Their litter sizes are larger. The average is about nine, but there can be as many as 13 kits. However, female stoats can only ever have one litter a year because they have to undergo delayed implantation. Matings take place in the summer and the ova are fertilised as normal. The fertile cells, known as blastocysts, then enter a state of suspended animation and it is not until the next spring that they implant in the uterus wall and develop fully. Births occur after a true gestation of four weeks, at least nine months after mating. This curious process is usually found in longer lived mustelids, such as pine martens and badgers, which mature later in life and have smaller litters. To enable stoats to capitalise rapidly on variable resources, they have evolved an ingenious response to the limitations of having a single litter.

Juvenile sex in stoats

The secret lies with the extraordinary sexual precociousness of young stoats. Shortly after an adult female has given birth, she comes into oestrus again and soon attracts the attention of male stoats. The males woo her, perhaps with gifts of prey brought to the den, giving rise to the myth of male parental care in stoats. When the adult female selects a suitable male, he is granted access to the den and mates with her. After mating with the adult female, he then mates with each of her blind, helpless daughters. This is obviously good news for the male, since he secures several matings from courting only a single female. The precocious young are also benefiting from this unusual arrangement. Despite their appearance, they are sexually mature, receptive and compliant to the male and actually seem to encourage his advances.

This is the perfect solution to the constraints of delayed implantation. In effect, every young female stoat is pregnant well before she even leaves the nest. This means that stoats are excellent colonisers of new habitats, since it only takes a single female to repopulate an area where a local extinction has taken place. It also means that if only one or two female stoats are missed by a predator control programme, there could be dozens of young born the next season to frustrate the gamekeeper's efforts.

Bacula help mating

Other aspects of reproduction in weasels and stoats are similar. Ovulation, the release of eggs from the ovaries, is stimulated by mating. As a result, mating is an exhausting and demanding task for male weasels and stoats. In order to assist in the prolonged coupling required to stimulate the female, male stoats and weasels are equipped with a penis bone, or baculum. This means that successful matings can last several hours, with the male keeping a tight grip on the female by grasping the scruff of her neck with his teeth.

Growing kits

Young weasels and stoats develop rapidly. They are born helpless and blind, with a characteristic mane of downy hair on the scruff of the neck. The female spends a great deal of time with them in the first few weeks of life, keeping them warm with her own body heat and defending them from predators and, in the case of stoats, unwanted suitors. When she leaves the nest the kits enter a temporary torpor, where body temperature drops and respiration slows, in order to conserve their meagre energy supplies until their mother returns. The kits' eyes open at about 30 days in weasels and 40 days in stoats, by which time they are also eating meat. Soon after, they begin to make their first forays out from the nest. As they develop, the mother spends less time with the kits and more time foraging to cater for their enormous appetites. Eventually they will venture further from the nest and start killing their own prey at about eight weeks in weasels and 11 weeks in stoats.

Young weasels of both sexes attain adult size and sexual maturity at an early age. The two sexes of stoat, on the other hand, mature quite differently. Females are sexually mature as nestlings and are fully grown by about six months. However, male stoats stay sexually immature and are smaller than mature adults, until they are nearly a year old.

Gangs of youths

Another aspect of the mythology surrounding stoats and weasels is explained by the increasing independence of the young. The so-called gangs of weasels and stoats that attacked Toad Hall, and are genuinely seen by gamekeepers and naturalists, are in fact family groups. Usually the mother is moving her litter from one disturbed den site to a safer location, but also troops of brothers and sisters can be seen making their first forays into the adult world. Stoats and weasels are, very rarely, reported to hunt in groups and it is almost certainly young siblings doing this. Families become increasingly intolerant of one another at about three months of age, and eventually the young disperse from the nest to find territories of their own and face the rigours of adult life. After dispersal, family ties break down and the only weasels and stoats seen together will be either fighting over territory or courting mates.

Moving house. If her den is disturbed a female stoat will often carry her kits one by one to a safer location. If threatened, she will defend her litter fearlessly.

Mortality

Starvation is the biggest threat

Many stoats and weasels don't survive their first year and only a minority are recruited into the breeding population. They are subject to a number of sources of mortality; starvation, predation and diseases all take their toll. Starvation is probably the most important cause of mortality in stoats and weasels and we have already seen how drastically food supply affects their numbers. In practice, food supply acts on populations at several stages. It can act on pregnant females by reducing the number of young they give birth to, perhaps even causing total reproductive failure. Kits can die before independence because of the female's inability to bring back enough food. Newly independent juveniles may die because the ranges they secure for themselves cannot provide enough food.

Predation by larger carnivores

Both stoats and weasels are also small enough to be eaten, or mistaken for prey, by a variety of larger predators including owls, kestrels and foxes. Domestic and feral cats are also frequent killers of stoats and weasels in Britain. It is unlikely that stoats and weasels make up a substantial part of the diet of any predator, but this does not mean that low levels of predation are not important. The risk of predation can strongly affect the behaviour of prey species. In much the same way that voles may suppress their breeding and mobility when the threat of predation is high, stoats and weasels may adapt to avoid the risk of predation themselves. One strong example highlights the importance of predation to stoat and weasel biology.

Tails I win

Vigilant. Stoats and weasels often stand up on their back legs to get a better perspective on their surroundings. This helps them to locate prey and guard against the threat of predation by larger animals.

Both stoats and long-tailed weasels have long tails with a black tip, while weasels have short, plain tails with no black tip. In a series of experiments using dummy mustelids and trained hawks, it was found that hawks were not at all successful at capturing either small animals with short, plain tails or larger animals with long, black tipped tails. In contrast, they were more successful at capturing small animals with short, black-tipped tails and larger animals with long, plain tails. The reason was that the hawks focused on the black tip when they swooped, but they only grasped the tip of the tail and the animals could slip away. The study concluded that stoats and long-tailed weasels had black tipped tails because their tails were long enough that the prominent tip was far away enough from the body to confuse potential predators. Weasels, on the other hand, do not have a long tail, perhaps because it would lose too much heat in winter, and a black tip could not be far away enough from the body to avoid predation. It is a simple idea but is a graphic illustration of how even rare events can affect stoat and weasel biology in the long term.

Mites, ticks and fleas

The burden of parasites infesting the skin, guts and other organs can be a major factor in controlling animal populations, by affecting their ability to reproduce and survive. Stoats and weasels are susceptible to infection by a range of parasites. These include lice, ticks, fleas and mites, which infest the skin and fur and are known as ectoparasites, and worms that infest the internal organs, known as endoparasites. Generally the burden of parasites in stoats and weasels seems comparatively low and there are only a few parasites that have evolved specifically to infect stoats and weasels. Perhaps the low density at which stoats and weasels live means that transmission of ectoparasites between individuals is rare. However, the parasite burden on some individuals can be very high. One female stoat carried over 1800 mite larvae, while another carried over 250 ticks. Stoats and weasels almost certainly pick up ectoparasites from the nests of other mammals. The importance of infection resulting from the use of other species' nests is shown by the contrast between the commonness of mole, squirrel and rat fleas on stoats and weasels compared to the rarity of these animals in stoat and weasel diet.

Unlike ectoparasites, endoparasites can cause major problems for stoats and weasels. Other predators such as red foxes carry a wide range of tapeworms and roundworms picked up from their prey, so it is surprising that stoats and weasels, which share much of their diet with other British predators, do not carry more worms. In examining the guts of over 900 stoats and weasels, we have only found adult tapeworms in a single individual.

Worms on the brain

However, one nematode roundworm infests the skulls of both weasels and stoats and is incredibly widespread. *Skrjabingylus nasicola* (pronounced Scra-bin-jile-us) is a particularly unpleasant parasite which is picked up by weasels and stoats as a larva. It then migrates to the nasal sinuses where it matures into a large worm that gradually erodes the bones of the skull. Eventually, lesions can appear which are clearly visible in cleaned skulls. On average, 82% of British weasels and between 17 and 30% of British stoats show damage to their skulls resulting from *Skrjabingylus* infection. Damp habitats favour the survival of the larvae while they are outside the host mammal's body and weasel populations in areas with high rainfall can experience up to 100% infestation.

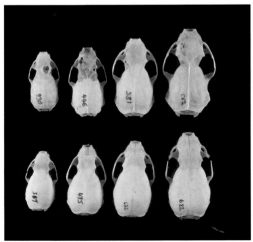

Stoat and weasel skulls. From left to right; female weasels, male weasels, female stoats, male stoats. The change in skull shape from young (below) to adult (above) animals can be used to distinguish age classes. In the adult animals, note the damage caused to the eye region by Skrjabingylus.

Skrjabingylus worms go through several stages in their life cycle, one of which is always in a mollusc such as a snail or a slug. Usually the mollusc is eaten by a predator and the adult worms infect this host. However, stoats and weasels rarely, if ever, eat slugs or snails. So, where do the worms come from? It appears that the worm larvae have an extra, intermediate stage of the cycle as cysts in the glands and muscles of mice and voles. These are commonly eaten by weasels and stoats and, when eaten, the larvae emerge from their cysts and progress to the sinus as usual. When skulls damaged by the parasites are examined, it is hard to imagine that the worms are not causing severe pain, and perhaps ultimately death, in the infected animals. However, animals with *Skrjabingylus* do not show any signs of poorer condition or higher mortality than those without.

Wildlife diseases Stoats and weasels also suffer from several other wildlife diseases. These include: canine distemper, which nearly wiped out the world's last colony of black-footed ferrets *Mustela nigripes* in America; tularaemia, a bacterial fever transmitted from rabbits and rodents by biting insects and ticks; sarcocystosis, a disease caused by the cysts of protozoa; and ringworm, a fungal skin disease. Recent studies in New Zealand have also occasionally found bovine tuberculosis in stoats and, more frequently, in feral ferrets *Mustela furo*. Tb has also been recorded in feral ferrets and polecats in Britain, but not in stoats or weasels. So, it seems unlikely that they are a significant vector of the disease in Britain.

Population structure

Sex ratio The sex ratio of stoats and weasels at birth is about 1:1. However, weasels and stoats trapped on British game estates usually have a ratio of males to females of about 3:1 and 2:1 respectively. It seems unlikely that there are differences in patterns of natural mortality between the sexes and, in collections of stoats shot by gamekeepers, the sex ratio is much closer to 1:1. The predominance of males in trapped samples is probably because females have smaller ranges than males and are less likely to wander beyond them. This means that they will have fewer traps in their range than males. If traps are set closer together, then more females will usually be caught. For this reason, live traps used in an ecological study must be set close together in order to ensure that both sexes are sampled evenly.

Ageing stoats and weasels Working out the age of live stoats and weasels is extremely problematic. It is relatively easy to distinguish between adults and juveniles just out of the nest, on the basis of their fur, small size and the shape of the skull. However, these differences rapidly disappear as the animals mature. Stoats in their first year of life can be identified by the undeveloped testes in males and the nipples, which are invisible in females. Juvenile weasels mature so quickly that the same technique cannot be applied. The degree of tooth wear may also be used as a rough guide to age, but there is no reliable way of ageing adult stoats and weasels when they are still alive.

The most accurate ageing techniques for stoats and weasels are based on dead animals. The morphology of the skull is a good guide. In young stoats and weasels it is rounded and bulbous at the back, there are open sutures between the bony plates of the skull, and the bone itself is quite porous and chalky in texture. In adults, the skull is more elongated, the sutures have fused and are invisible, and the bone is solid and glossy. In addition, the constriction in the skull that lies behind the eye socket narrows as animals get older. The sagittal crest that runs along the top of the skull also becomes more pronounced with age. In male stoats and weasels, the weight of the baculum increases under the influence of testosterone, probably throughout the animal's life.

For most purposes, it may be sufficient to distinguish only three age classes: juvenile, sub-adult and adult. Using a combination of skull characters, baculum weight and a set of photographs of skulls from animals of known age, it is possible accurately to distinguish between adults and young up to about eight months of age, though this varies between the sexes and species. If the date of death is also known, the age can be worked out by subtracting an average birth date for the population in the area being examined. For weasels in Britain this is usually taken as 1st June and for stoats 1st April. Unfortunately, adult stoats can only be aged accurately by extracting and sectioning a tooth and counting the annual layers in the cementum that joins the tooth to the jaw. This technique is probably valid for weasels as well but has yet to be tested on weasels of known age.

Age structure
Life expectancy for stoats and weasels is very low and most animals are under one year old when they die. The average age at death is between nine and 11 months in weasels and 11 and 16 months in stoats. While captive stoats and weasels can live for up to ten years, the oldest weasel recorded in the wild in Britain was less than three years old, while the oldest wild stoat was four and a half. Populations of weasels and stoats are, therefore, always made up of a large proportion of juveniles and sub adults. The actual proportion of animals less than one year old varies, but can be as much as 84% in weasels and up to 90% in stoats.

Activity, territories and ranges

The spatial behaviour of stoats and weasels is probably the single most frustrating aspect of their biology to study. Because their populations are so variable in size and there are regular extinctions and recolonisations, density is perpetually changing and territories and home ranges are rarely held for more than a few months.

Live trapping
Apart from tracking footprints in snow, which depends on long term snow cover, there are two main methods of studying ranging behaviour. The first method is an extension of a live trapping programme, where the animals are captured, marked and recaptured. They are marked with ear tags or, for weasels only, photographed so they can be recognised on the basis of their individual fur patterns. Subsequent recaptures are plotted to form a map that represents the minimum area that the animals occupy. Unfortunately this simple technique has several inherent problems. It can be virtually impossible to capture and recapture enough animals. Some animals are naturally cautious of traps and others become trap shy after being caught once. Animals also have a habit of losing tags and of simply abandoning their ranges altogether. Furthermore, the maximum extent of an animal's range is rarely the same as the extent of the trapping scheme. Having said that, this technique provided the first information on weasel ranges in Britain and was also used in a recent Canadian study of stoat ranges.

Radio tracking

Alternatively, animals can be tagged with a radio transmitter. This allows the animals' movements to be studied in much greater detail and is really the only accurate method available. Unfortunately, the problems of live trapping still apply, and tracking of stoats and weasels is particularly frustrating and much more difficult than for other, larger animals. The collars have to be very small and so are expensive, while the power and life of the transmitter is limited. For a small animal that is either close to, or under the ground, the signal can be difficult to pick up and hard to follow. Because of the short life of the battery the animals also have to be recaptured every month or two to fit a new collar.

Food or sex?

Two factors influence stoat and weasel ranging behaviour: food and reproduction. At different times of the year, the importance of the two resources changes. In the autumn and winter territories are marked out using scent from the anal glands and are defended energetically against members of the same sex. At this time, stoat and weasel society is comprised of large male territories, encompassing the territories of several females as well as a number of wandering young males with no fixed range.

Woodland and farmland ranges

Weasel ranges were first studied in Britain in young conifer plantations with rides of rank grass and large field vole populations. In areas with such rich food supplies, male weasel ranges were as small as 1-5 hectares while females occupied less than one hectare. Two similar studies in Wytham, near Oxford, looked at the range size of weasels in woodland and on farmland. The first study used live trapping and worked out that range size for resident male weasels was 7-15 hectares, while females used only 1-4 hectares. The second study used radio-tracking and found that male weasels occupied ranges on farmland of up to 190 hectares. On farmland food is concentrated around hedgerows and field margins and so the weasels rarely ventured more than a few metres away from linear features. When range size was recalculated by measuring the area of a corridor of

Hedgerow corridors. Hedgerows and uncultivated field margins, such as this conservation headland, provide quality habitat for stoats and weasels in arable landscapes, and they rarely venture more than a few metres out into the open fields.

ten metres around hedges, thereby excluding the unproductive centres of fields, weasel ranges on farmland were less than ten hectares. There has only been one study of stoat home ranges in Britain and that was on farmland in Scotland. This study found that a single male stoat, that was radio-tracked for ten days, had a range of over 250 hectares while three female stoats had an average range of 114 hectares.

In spring and summer, the importance of food increases for female stoats and weasels, since they must provide enough energy for themselves and their litter. In contrast, the males, which have no role in rearing the young, find that food is plentiful, but that receptive mates are unpredictable and hard to come by. Many animals that vigorously defended territories to protect their food supply now more or less abandon their territories for a nomadic lifestyle in pursuit of as many females as possible.

Roamers, stayers and transients

This switch in the importance of resources from food to mates happens over a matter of a few days and has a dramatic effect on male range size. In Sweden, male stoat ranges increased up to 50 times during spring and summer. The older, dominant males extended their ranges the most and roamed widely spending a few days with each female they encountered. Younger males were either stationary, staying in a small, distinct range throughout the spring, or transient, wandering continually with no distinct range. The success of each of the three strategies, roamers, stayers and transients, depended on social status. The roamers were dominant over most other males and stood the best chance of mating success, even though it was difficult to defend their expanded ranges. Stayers could mate successfully if the females resident in their area happened to come into oestrus when no roamers were around. The lowest status animals were transients which were subordinate to all other males but might occasionally be successful with a female in the absence of more dominant animals.

Nocturnal or not

Radio-tracking has also been used to describe the daily patterns of activity in stoats and weasels, which used to be thought to be nocturnal. We now know better. Stoats and weasels are active throughout the 24 hour period, in bouts of about 40 minutes separated by rest periods of one to four hours. Stoats and weasels tend to be more active during daylight in summer and more nocturnal in winter.

Conservation and management

Track counts

Monitoring populations of weasels and stoats is very difficult. Snow tracking can be used as a relative index of stoat and weasel abundance. A similar method has been used in New Zealand, except instead of snow counts, footprints are counted in tunnels equipped with waterproof ink pads and tracking papers. This method relies on the natural curiosity of stoats and weasels and their tendency to investigate every cavity they encounter. It has been tried in Britain, but in some areas the papers are quickly obliterated by the tracks of small rodents and it can be difficult to pick out mustelid tracks. A very labour intensive way of monitoring populations is by trying to live trap the animals and conducting a capture-mark-recapture experiment, but it is extremely hard work.

Game bags

The best way of monitoring populations is, therefore, to capitalise on data collected by gamekeepers, many of whom maintain accurate records of the numbers of weasels and stoats they kill every year. Because trapping does not greatly affect overall stoat and weasel numbers, their records can be used as an index of the relative abundance of animals that year.

Historical rivalry. Gamekeepers' gibbets were once used to keep a tally of the animals they trapped. Gibbets have now virtually disappeared from the countryside but the records kept by gamekeepers are a valuable source of data on stoat and weasel populations. This 1968 photograph shows a weasel and two stoats on what was then a typical gibbet.

When records for single estates are examined, it is remarkable just how variable local populations are. A particularly long set of records from a large estate in Suffolk graphically illustrates the relationship between stoats and rabbits. The effect of myxomatosis in the 1950s is particularly noticeable and both rabbits and stoats declined dramatically in this period. Interestingly, weasels increased during myxomatosis. Because of a reduction in the pressure of rabbit grazing, rough grassland reappeared and vole populations increased. This meant that there was more food available for weasels and populations boomed for a few years.

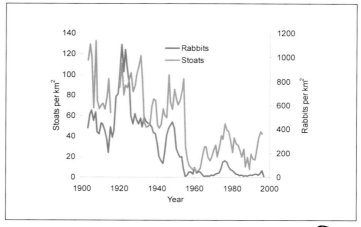

Stoat and rabbit bags. Long term records from a Suffolk estate show the marked fluctuations in stoat populations and the close relationship between rabbit and stoat numbers. The crash in rabbit numbers brought about by myxomatosis in the 1950s was followed soon after by a steep decline in the number of stoats trapped.

The Game Conservancy Trust has collated gamekeepers' trapping and shooting records since 1960, as part of their National Game Bag Census. These archives can be used to describe national trends in weasel and stoat bags by calculating the average numbers trapped per square kilometre over all contributing estates. These figures must be interpreted with some caution since the averages contain some potential sources of confusion. Firstly, the numbers caught depend on the effort being put into trapping. If some factor reduces the effort being put into trapping, such as increasing reliance on reared game, then the number of animals killed will decline. Also, trapping records are affected by the number of gamekeepers working and this has been in decline in Britain for many years. Despite these potential problems, the National Game Bag Census is probably the best index we have of national populations of stoats and weasels.

Declining weasels?

The average number of weasels killed by gamekeepers has been in decline since the start of the Census scheme. By comparison, stoat numbers increased until the mid-1970s but have been declining slightly since then. Up to this point, there had been a close relationship between stoat and rabbit numbers. Since rabbit numbers continued to increase, dramatically so in the early 1990s, it might be expected that stoat numbers would have matched this leap in the numbers of their prey. Since they did not, it appears that some factor is preventing an increase in stoat populations. We are left with an overall picture of a decline in the weasel bag and a stoat bag that is smaller than perhaps it should be.

Average stoat and weasel bags. The National Game Bag Census summarises changes in the average number of weasels and stoats killed per square kilometre by gamekeepers. Weasel bags have been in steady decline since 1960. Stoat bags increased until the mid 1970s but have decreased slowly since, in contrast to dramatically increasing rabbit bags.

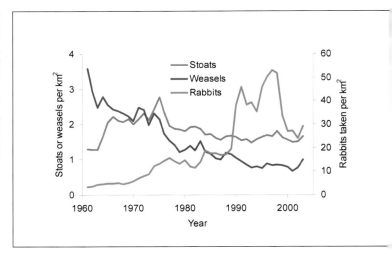

There are several possible explanations for this. First, less effort may be put into trapping weasels and stoats because of increasing reliance on reared game. Therefore, the national average bag of both species would be expected to decline. Second, weasel numbers would be expected to decline as rabbit numbers recovered from their crash during myxomatosis. As increasing numbers of rabbits graze down rough grass, vole populations drop and there is less food for weasels. Alternatively, it is possible that some other factor is actually reducing weasel numbers and inhibiting population growth in stoats.

The first two explanations for changes in the stoat and weasel record are certainly likely to be important, but it is possible that the latter is also true. If so, then there is some cause for concern. There are several problems facing stoat and weasel populations and which could be causing a general decline. These include; increasing numbers of other predators, environmental pollution and habitat loss.

Foxes reduce stoats and weasels

Red foxes are probably increasing in Britain and they are known to have a negative effect on stoat and weasel populations. In a Dutch study, stoats disappeared from an area of sand dunes, where they had formerly been abundant, shortly after the arrival of foxes. An American study also showed that where fox numbers were high, weasel and stoat numbers were low and vice versa. Foxes have also been shown to have a negative effect on other mustelids such as pine martens. This interaction between members of groups of ecologically similar species is known as intraguild predation and is becoming increasingly recognised as an important factor in controlling the structure of wildlife communities.

Environmental pollution

Environmental pollution has caused the dramatic decline of other predatory species in the past. The growth of otter populations has been inhibited by the pollution of rivers and lakes by PCBs. Sparrowhawk numbers crashed in the 1960s following the widespread use of DDT as an agricultural pesticide. Stoats and weasels may also be affected by pesticides applied to control agricultural pests. Anticoagulant rodenticides are applied on 70-80% of British farms in order to control rats and grey squirrels. Stoats and weasels are unlikely to eat the rodenticide baits directly and do not eat rats or squirrels very often. However, non-target species such as wood mice and bank voles will also eat the baits and act as

Arable desert. The intensification of agriculture has meant the removal of thousands of kilometres of hedgerows that provided food and cover for stoats and weasels.

a source of secondary poisoning when they in turn are eaten by stoats and weasels. As a result, a substantial proportion of stoats and weasels from parts of England also contain traces of these rodenticides. Anticoagulant rodenticides are highly toxic to stoats and weasels. In a New Zealand trial, a sample of 11 stoats and one weasel that had been tagged with radio collars had all been poisoned only nine days after the large-scale application of rodenticide baits. Perhaps even more important than lethal poisoning are the effects of long-term exposure to sub-lethal doses of rodenticides. If the body condition and reproductive capacity of female stoats and weasels is reduced by sub-lethal doses, then they may be unable to produce as many young as are needed to maintain the population.

Habitat loss

Perhaps the greatest area for conservation concern is the widespread and drastic changes to the British landscape brought about by intensive farming. Many species of birds and mammals have declined following the loss of hedgerows, woodlands and rough, uncultivated ground as agricultural demands on the land increase. On farmland, hedgerows are an essential habitat for stoats and weasels, since they provide food and cover from larger predators. Hedgerows were still being removed at a rate of 20,000 kilometres a year in the early 1990s. Likewise, the loss of rough grassland with its high vole populations will affect both species, particularly weasels, since they are so dependent on voles for successful reproduction. Drainage and cultivation of rough grassland has been one of the major factors contributing to the decline of another vole predator, the barn owl.

Habitat loss may also act in a more subtle way to reduce stoat and weasel populations. Since hedgerows are important for providing cover against predators, they may be important for providing a route for animals to disperse between isolated populations. If hedgerows or other dispersal routes are lost, stoats and weasels may be at greater risk from predators and recolonisation of some areas may be made more difficult.

Conclusion

Future work

Stoats and weasels are such frustrating animals to study that many projects only scratch the surface of their complex behaviour and interactions with the environment. Despite being common and widespread in Britain, there are still a great many aspects of stoat and weasel biology that remain to be explained by scientists and naturalists. The factors governing body size and reproduction are of great interest to biologists concerned with evolutionary processes, while conservationists and wildlife managers need a good deal more information about the general ecology of stoats and weasels. Of particular interest would be information about the effects of habitat changes and pesticides on populations and more detailed data are certainly needed on litter sizes, the dispersal of young animals and the various factors that influence ranging behaviour and movement patterns.

Upbeat lifestyle

Stoats and weasels have evolved a wide range of extraordinary adaptations to their small size and their upbeat lifestyle as predators of small mammals. They could, with more research, begin to provide excellent models for understanding a great deal more about evolution and ecological processes in the widest context.

Acknowledgements

We are very grateful to the following for their kind permission to use their photographs; Stephen Dalton/NHPA (p. 14), Manfred Danegger/NHPA (Cover and p. 1), Vanessa Latford (p. 3), Graeme McLaren (p. 25 and 30), Pat Morris (p. 13 and 18), Christopher Perrins (p. 15), Stephen Tapper/The Game Conservancy Trust (p. 17), Roger Tidman/NHPA (p. 20), University of Bristol Library Special Collections (p. 6) and The Vincent Wildlife Trust for the photographs of Frank Greenaway (p. 8, 10, 21 and 30). Other photographs are the copyright of the authors. We are greatly indebted to The Dulverton Trust, English Nature, The People's Trust for Endangered Species and The Wingate Foundation for financial support; to Carolyn King for her valuable comments on a draft of this booklet; to the many gamekeepers who have helped Robbie McDonald's studies, especially Jake Fiennes, Alan Garman, Howard Linge, Alan Smith, Robin Tingley and Lindsay Waddell; to Nicholas Aebischer of The Game Conservancy Trust for National Game Bag Census data; and to Charlotte Webbon, Glen Robson and David Macdonald for unpublished information. Finally, we would like to thank Sarah Wroot for her excellent line drawings.

Further reading and information

An excellent book and the definitive monograph on weasels and stoats is *The Natural History of Weasels and Stoats* by Carolyn King. Christopher Helm, London. 1989.

An accessible account of the weasel sub-family is *Stoats and Weasels Polecats and Martens* by Paddy Sleeman. Whittet Books, London. 1989.

Comprehensive accounts on all British mammals can be found in *The Handbook of British Mammals* edited by Gordon Corbet and Stephen Harris. Blackwell Science, Oxford. 1991.

An interesting account of experiences keeping a pet weasel can be found in *A Weasel in My Meatsafe* by Phil Drabble. Michael Joseph, London 1957.

www.mammal.org.uk The home page of The Mammal Society.

www.doc.govt.nz The New Zealand Department of Conservation page describes the problems caused to native wildlife by introduced stoats.